ENGLISH
NURSERY RHYMES

Illustrations by Luc Degryse

SING
A
SONG
OF
SIXPENCE

DISCOVERY BOOKS

ISBN: 1-55013-540-6

Discovery Books
70 The Esplanade
Toronto, Ontario
Canada M5E 1R2

Printed and bound in Hungary

93 94 95 96 6 5 4 3 2 1

CONTENTS

I won't be my father's Jack,
I won't be my mother's Jill;
I will be the fiddler's wife
And have music when I will.
T'have a little tune,
T'have a little tune,
Pretty love play me,
T'have a little tune.

*W*e are the music makers who come from London town,
We are the music makers who come from London town.
We can play on the pia-pia-piano,
We can play on the pia-pia-piano.
    We can dance hopsallah, hopsallah, hopsallah,
    And we can dance hopsallah, hopsallah.

We are the music makers who come from London town,
We are the music makers who come from London town.
We can play on the ha-ha-ha-ha-harmonica,
We can play on the ha-ha-ha-ha-harmonica.
    We can dance hopsallah, hopsallah, hopsallah,
    And we can dance hopsallah, hopsallah.

We are the music makers who come from London town,
We are the music makers who come from London town.
We can play on the pica-pica-piccolo,
We can play on the pica-pica-piccolo.
    We can dance hopsallah, hopsallah, hopsallah,
    And we can dance hopsallah, hopsallah.

We are the music makers who come from London town,
We are the music makers who come from London town.
We can play on the big, big, big bass drum,
We can play on the big, big, big bass drum.
    We can dance hopsallah, hopsallah, hopsallah,
    And we can dance hopsallah, hopsallah.

*B*oys and girls, come out to play,
The moon doth shine as bright as day.
Leave your supper and leave your sleep,
And join your playfellows in the street.
Come with a whoop and come with a call,
Come with a good will or not at all.
Up the ladder and down the wall,
A half-penny loaf will serve us all.
You'll find milk, and I'll find flour,
And we'll have a pudding in half an hour.

*E*eny, meeny, miny, mo,
Catch a tiger by the toe;
If he squeals, let him go,
Eeny, meeny, miny, mo.

*U*p and down the City Road,
In and out the Eagle,
That's the way the money goes,
Pop goes the weasel!

Half a pound of tuppenny rice,
Half a pound of treacle,
Mix it up and make it nice,
Pop goes the weasel!

Every night when I go out
The monkey's on the table;
Take a stick and knock it off,
Pop goes the weasel!

Hot cross buns! Hot cross buns!
One a penny, two a penny,
Hot cross buns!
If you have no daughters,
Give them to your sons,
One a penny, two a penny,
Hot cross buns!

Do you know the muffin man,
The muffin man, the muffin man?
Do you know the muffin man,
Who lives in Drury Lane?

Yes, I know the muffin man,
The muffin man, the muffin man.
Yes, I know the muffin man,
Who lives in Drury Lane.

Cobbler, cobbler, mend my shoe,
Get it done by half past two;
My toe is peeping through,
Cobbler, cobbler, mend my shoe.

Rub-a-dub-dub,
Three men in a tub;
And who do you think they be?
The butcher, the baker,
The candlestick-maker;
They all jumped out of a rotten potato,
Turn'em out, knaves all three!

*L*avender's blue, dilly, dilly,
Lavender's green;
When I am king, dilly, dilly,
You shall be queen.

Who told you so, dilly, dilly,
Who told you so?
'Twas mine own heart, dilly, dilly,
That told me so.

Call up your men, dilly, dilly,
Set them to work,
Some to the plough, dilly, dilly,
Some to the cart.

Some to make hay, dilly, dilly,
Some to cut corn,
While you and I, dilly, dilly,
Keep ourselves warm.

*S*ee-saw, sacradown,
Which is the way to London Town?
One foot up and the other foot down,
That is the way to London Town.

*T*o market, to market, to buy a fat pig,
Home again, home again, jiggety-jig.
To market, to market, to buy a fat hog,
Home again, home again, jiggety-jog.

*R*ide a cock-horse to Banbury Cross,
To see a fine lady upon a white horse;
With rings on her fingers and bells on her toes,
She shall have music wherever she goes.

Doctor Foster went to Gloucester
In a shower of rain;
He stepped in a puddle, right up to his middle,
And never went there again.

*I*ncy Wincy spider
Climbed up the water spout;
Down came the rain
And washed the spider out;
Out came the sun
And dried up all the rain;
And Incy Wincy spider
Climbed up the spout again.

*R*ain, rain, go away,
Come again another day;
Rain, rain, go away,
Come on mother's washing-day!

*I*t's raining, it's pouring,
The old man is snoring;
He went to bed
And bumped his head
And couldn't get up in the morning.

*L*ondon Bridge is falling down,
Falling down, falling down,
London Bridge is falling down,
My fair lady.

Build it up with wood and clay,
Wood and clay, wood and clay,
Build it up with wood and clay,
My fair lady.

Wood and clay will wash away,
Wash away, wash away,
Wood and clay will wash away,
My fair lady.

Build it up with bricks and mortar,
Bricks and mortar, bricks and mortar,
Build it up with bricks and mortar,
My fair lady.

Bricks and mortar will not stay,
Will not stay, will not stay,
Bricks and mortar will not stay,
My fair lady.

Build it up with iron and steel,
Iron and steel, iron and steel,
Build it up with iron and steel,
My fair lady.

Iron and steel will bend and bow,
Bend and bow, bend and bow,
Iron and steel will bend and bow,
My fair lady.

Build it up with silver and gold,
Silver and gold, silver and gold,
Build it up with silver and gold,
My fair lady.

Silver and gold will be stolen away,
Stolen away, stolen away,
Silver and gold will be stolen away,
My fair lady.

Set a man to watch all night,
Watch all night, watch all night,
Set a man to watch all night,
My fair lady.

Suppose the man should fall asleep,
Fall asleep, fall asleep,
Suppose the man should fall asleep,
My fair lady?

Give him a pipe to smoke all night,
Smoke all night, smoke all night,
Give him a pipe to smoke all night,
My fair lady.

*R*ing-a-ring o'roses,
A pocket full of posies,
A-tishoo, a-tishoo,
We all fall down.

The king has sent his daughter
To fetch a pail of water,
A-tishoo, a-tishoo,
We all fall down.

The robin on the steeple
Sits high above the people,
A-tishoo, a-tishoo,
We all fall down.

The wedding bells are ringing,
The boys and girls are singing,
A-tishoo, a-tishoo,
We all fall down.

*P*olly, put the kettle on,
Polly, put the kettle on,
Polly, put the kettle on,
We'll all have tea.

Sukey, take it off again,
Sukey, take it off again,
Sukey, take it off again,
They've all gone away.

Dance to your daddy,
My little laddie,
Dance to your daddy,
My little lad.

You shall have a fishy,
On a little dishy,
You shall have a fishy,
When the boat comes in.

Dance to your daddy,
My little lassie,
Dance to your daddy,
My little lass.

You shall have a fishy,
On a little dishy,
You shall have a fishy,
When the boat comes in.

Handy Spandy, Jack-a-dandy
Loves plum cake and sugar candy.
He bought some at the grocer's shop
And out he came, hop, hop, hop.

This little pig went to market,
This little pig stayed at home,
This little pig had roast beef,
This little pig had none,
And this little pig cried wee, wee, wee,
All the way home.

Jack and Jill went up the hill
To fetch a pail of water;
Jack fell down and broke his crown
And Jill came tumbling after.

Up Jack got and home did trot
As fast as he could caper;
Went to bed and bound his head
With vinegar and brown paper.

When Jill came in how she did grin
To see Jack's paper plaster;
Mother vexed, did whip her next
For causing Jack's disaster.

Jeremiah, blow the fire,
Puff, puff, puff!
First you blow it gently,
Then you blow it rough.

Curly Locks, Curly Locks,
Wilt thou be mine?
Thou shalt not wash dishes
Nor yet feed the swine;
But sit on a cushion
And sew a fine seam,
And feed upon strawberries,
Sugar and cream.

Georgie Porgie, pudding and pie,
Kissed the girls and made them cry;
When the boys came out to play,
Georgie Porgie ran away.

Little Jack Horner
Sat in a corner
Eating a Christmas pie.
He put in his thumb
And pulled out a plum,
And said, What a good boy am I!

Mary had a little lamb,
Its fleece was white as snow;
And everywhere that Mary went
The lamb was sure to go.

It followed her to school one day,
That was against the rule;
It made the children laugh and play
To see a lamb at school.

And so the teacher turned it out,
But still it lingered near;
And waited patiently about
Till Mary did appear.

Why does the lamb love Mary so?
The eager children cry;
Why, Mary loves the lamb, you know,
The teacher did reply.

Bobby Shafto's gone to sea,
Silver buckles at his knee;
He'll come back and marry me,
Bonny Bobby Shafto!

Bobby Shafto's bright and fair,
Combing down his yellow hair;
He's my love for evermore,
Bonny Bobby Shafto!

Bobby Shafto's looking out,
All his ribbons flew about;
All the ladies gave a shout,
Hey for Bobby Shafto!

Old Mother Hubbard
She went to the cupboard
To fetch her poor dog a bone,
But when she got there
The cupboard was bare,
And so the poor dog had none.

She went to the baker's
To buy him some bread,
But when she came back
The poor dog was dead.

She went to the joiner's
To buy him a coffin,
But when she came back
The poor dog was laughing.

She went to the fishmonger's
To buy him some fish,
But when she came back
He was licking the dish.

She went to the hatter's
To buy him a hat,
But when she came back
He was feeding the cat.

She went to the barber's
To buy him a wig,
But when she came back
He was dancing a jig.

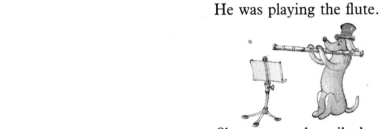

She went to the fruiterer's
To buy him some fruit,
But when she came back
He was playing the flute.

She went to the tailor's
To buy him a coat,
But when she came back
He was riding a goat.

She went to the cobbler's
To buy him some shoes,
But when she came back
He was reading the news.

The dame made a curtsey,
The dog made a bow;
The dame said, Your servant,
The dog said, Bow-wow.

I do not like thee, Doctor Fell,
The reason why I cannot tell;
But this I know, and know full well,
I do not like thee, Doctor Fell.

Gregory Griggs, Gregory Griggs,
Had twenty-seven different wigs.
He wore them up, he wore them down,
To please the people of the town;
He wore them east, he wore them west,
But he never could tell which he liked best.

Old King Cole
Was a merry old soul,
And a merry old soul was he;
He called for his pipe,
And he called for his drum,
And he called for his fiddlers three.

Every drummer, he had a fine drum
And a very fine drum had he;
Tumty-tum, tumty-tum,
Tumty-tum, tumty-tum,
And a very fine drum had he.

Every fiddler, he had a fine fiddle,
And a very fine fiddle had he;
Oh, there's none so rare
As can compare
With King Cole and his fiddlers three.

Oh, the grand old Duke of York,
He had ten thousand men:
He marched them up to the top of the hill,
And he marched them down again.
And when they were up, they were up,
And when they were down, they were down,
And when they were only half way up,
They were neither up nor down.

Humpty Dumpty sat on a wall,
Humpty Dumpty had a great fall;
All the King's horses and all the King's men
Couldn't put Humpty together again.

One, two,
　　Buckle my shoe;
Three, four,
　　Knock at the door;
Five, six,
　　Pick up sticks;
Seven, eight,
　　Lay them straight;
Nine, ten,
　　A big fat hen;
Eleven, twelve,
　　Dig and delve;
Thirteen, fourteen,
　　Maids a-courting;
Fifteen, sixteen,
　　Maids in the kitchen;
Seventeen, eighteen,
　　Maids in waiting;
Nineteen, twenty,
　　My plate's empty.

Pussy cat, pussy cat, where have you been?
I've been to London to visit the Queen.
Pussy cat, pussy cat, what did you there?
I frightened a little mouse under her chair.

Hickory, dickory, dock,
The mouse ran up the clock,
The clock struck one,
The mouse ran down,
Hickory, dickory, dock.

*I*ckle ockle, blue bockle,
   Fishes in the sea,
If you want a pretty maid,
   Please choose me.

*B*aa, baa, black sheep,
Have you any wool?
Yes, sir, yes, sir,
Three bags full;
One for the master,
And one for the dame,
One for the little boy
Who lives down the lane.

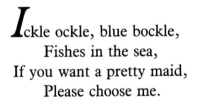

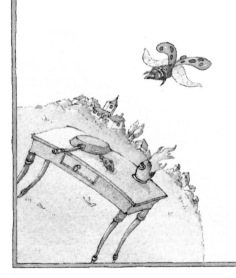

*L*adybird, ladybird, fly away home,
Your house is on fire, your children are gone;
All but one and her name is Ann,
And she has crept under the frying-pan.

Solomon Grundy,
Born on Monday,
Christened on Tuesday,
Married on Wednesday,
Took ill on Thursday,
Worse on Friday,
Died on Saturday,
Buried on Sunday,
This is the end
Of Solomon Grundy.

Sing a song of sixpence,
A pocket full of rye;
Four and twenty blackbirds
Baked in a pie.

When the pie was opened
The birds began to sing;
Wasn't that a dainty dish
To set before the king?

The king was in his counting-house
Counting out his money;
The queen was in the parlour
Eating bread and honey.

The maid was in the garden
Hanging out the clothes,
When down came a blackbird,
And pecked off her nose.

*T*hirty days hath September,
April, June and November;
All the rest have thirty-one,
Excepting February alone,
And that has twenty-eight days clear
And twenty-nine in each leap year.

A dillar, a dollar,
A ten o'clock scholar,
What makes you come so soon?
You used to come at ten o'clock,
But now you come at noon.

*I*f all the world were paper,
And all the sea were ink,
If all the trees were bread and cheese,
What should we have to drink?

One, two, three, four, five,
Once I caught a fish alive,
Six, seven, eight, nine, ten,
Then I let it go again.

Why did you let it go?
Because it bit my finger so.
Which finger did it bite?
This little finger on the right.

Monday's child is fair of face,
Tuesday's child is full of grace,
Wednesday's child is full of woe,
Thursday's child has far to go,
Friday's child is loving and giving,
Saturday's child works hard for a living,
And the child that is born on the Sabbath day
Is bonny and blithe and good and gay.

One for sorrow,
Two for joy,
Three for a girl,
Four for a boy,
Five for silver,
Six for gold,
Seven for a secret never to be told.

A was an apple pie,
B bit it,
C cut it,
D dealt it,
E's eaten it,
F fought for it,
G got it,
H had it,
I inspected it,
J jumped for it,
K kept it,
L longed for it,
M mourned for it,
N nodded at it,
O opened it,
P peeped at it,
Q quartered it,
R ran for it,
S stole it,
T took it,
U upset it,
V viewed it,
W wanted it,
X, Y, Z and ampersand
All wished for a piece in hand.

*L*ittle Miss Muffet
Sat on a tuffet,
Eating her curds and whey;
There came a big spider
Who sat down beside her,
And frightened Miss Muffet away.

*P*ease porridge hot,
Pease porridge cold,
Pease porridge in the pot,
Nine days old.

Some like it hot,
Some like it cold,
Some like it in the pot,
Nine days old.

There was a crooked man
     And he walked a crooked mile;
He found a crooked sixpence
     Against a crooked stile;
He bought a crooked cat
     Which caught a crooked mouse,
And they all lived together
     In a little crooked house.

The man in the moon
Came down too soon,
And asked his way to Norwich;
He went by the south,
And burnt his mouth
With eating cold plum porridge.

Hey diddle, diddle,
The cat and the fiddle,
The cow jumped over the moon;
The little dog laughed
To see such sport,
And the dish ran away with the spoon.

Oh that I were
Where I would be;
Then would I be
Where I am not.
But where I am,
There I must be,
And where I would be,
I cannot.

This old man, he played one,
He played knick-knack on my drum,
With a knick-knack, paddy whack,
Give a dog a bone,
This old man came rolling home.

This old man, he played two,
He played knick-knack on my shoe,
With a knick-knack, paddy whack,
Give a dog a bone,
This old man came rolling home.

This old man, he played three,
He played knick-knack on my knee,
With a knick-knack, paddy whack,
Give a dog a bone,
This old man came rolling home.

This old man, he played four,
He played knick-knack on my door,
With a knick-knack, paddy whack,
Give a dog a bone,
This old man came rolling home.

This old man, he played five,
He played knick-knack on my hive,
With a knick-knack, paddy whack,
Give a dog a bone,
This old man came rolling home.

This old man, he played six,
He played knick-knack on my sticks,
With a knick-knack, paddy whack,
Give a dog a bone,
This old man came rolling home.

This old man, he played seven,
He played knick-knack up to heaven,
With a knick-knack, paddy whack,
Give a dog a bone,
This old man came rolling home.

This old man, he played eight,
He played knick-knack on my gate,
With a knick-knack, paddy whack,
Give a dog a bone,
This old man came rolling home.

This old man, he played nine,
He played knick-knack on my spine,
With a knick-knack, paddy whack,
Give a dog a bone,
This old man came rolling home.

This old man, he played ten,
He played knick-knack on my hen,
With a knick-knack, paddy whack,
Give a dog a bone,
This old man came rolling home.

On the first day of Christmas,
My true love sent to me
    A partridge in a pear tree.

On the second day of Christmas,
My true love sent to me
    Two turtle doves and
    A partridge in a pear tree.

On the third day of Christmas,
My true love sent to me
    Three French hens,
    Two turtle doves and
    A partridge in a pear tree.

On the fourth day of Christmas,
My true love sent to me
    Four colly birds,
    Three French hens,
    Two turtle doves and
    A partridge in a pear tree.

On the fifth day of Christmas,
My true love sent to me
    Five gold rings,
    Four colly birds,
    Three French hens,
    Two turtle doves and
    A partridge in a pear tree.

On the sixth day of Christmas,
My true love sent to me
Six geese a-laying,
Five gold rings,
Four colly birds,
Three French hens,
Two turtle doves and
A partridge in a pear tree.

On the seventh day of Christmas,
My true love sent to me
Seven swans a-swimming,
Six geese a-laying,
Five gold rings,
Four colly birds,
Three French hens,
Two turtle doves and
A partridge in a pear tree.

On the eighth day of Christmas,
My true love sent to me
Eight maids a-milking,
Seven swans a-swimming,
Six geese a-laying,
Five gold rings,
Four colly birds,
Three French hens,
Two turtle doves and
A partridge in a pear tree.

On the ninth day of Christmas,
My true love sent to me
Nine drummers drumming,
Eight maids a-milking,
Seven swans a-swimming,
Six geese a-laying,
Five gold rings,
Four colly birds,
Three French hens,
Two turtle doves and
A partridge in a pear tree.

On the tenth day of Christmas,
My true love sent to me
Ten pipers piping,
Nine drummers drumming,
Eight maids a-milking,
Seven swans a-swimming,
Six geese a-laying,
Five gold rings,
Four colly birds,
Three French hens,
Two turtle doves and
A partridge in a pear tree.

On the eleventh day of Christmas,
My true love sent to me
Eleven ladies dancing,
Ten pipers piping,
Nine drummers drumming,
Eight maids a-milking,
Seven swans a-swimming,
Six geese a-laying,
Five gold rings,
Four colly birds,
Three French hens,
Two turtle doves and
A partridge in a pear tree.

On the twelfth day of Christmas,
My true love sent to me
Twelve lords a-leaping,
Eleven ladies dancing,
Ten pipers piping,
Nine drummers drumming,
Eight maids a-milking,
Seven swans a-swimming,
Six geese a-laying,
Five gold rings,
Four colly birds,
Three French hens,
Two turtle doves and
A partridge in a pear tree.

Dame, get up and bake your pies,
Bake your pies, bake your pies,
Dame, get up and bake your pies
On Christmas day in the morning.

Dame, what makes your maidens lie,
Maidens lie, maidens lie,
Dame, what makes your maidens lie
On Christmas day in the morning.

Dame, what makes your ducks to die,
Ducks to die, ducks to die,
Dame, what makes your ducks to die
On Christmas day in the morning.

Their wings are cut, they cannot fly,
Cannot fly, cannot fly,
Their wings are cut, they cannot fly
On Christmas day in the morning.

Dame, get up and bake your pies
Bake your pies, bake your pies,
Dame, get up and bake your pies,
On Christmas day in the morning.

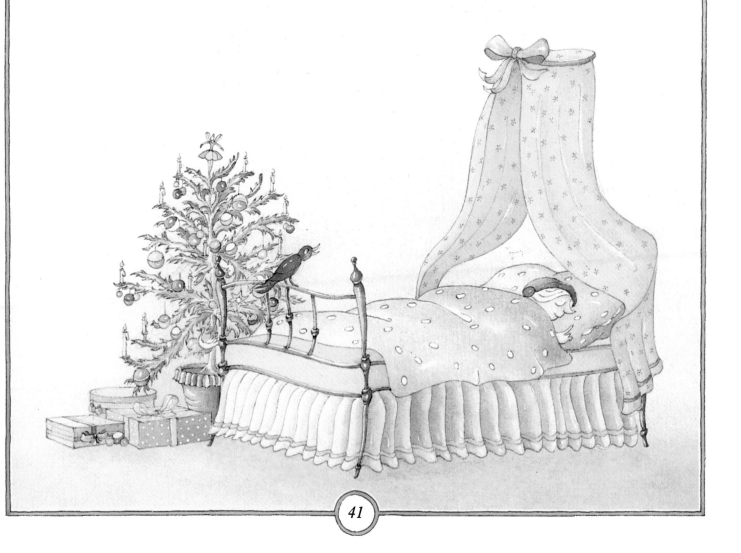

*G*o to bed late,
Stay very small;
Go to bed early,
Grow very tall.

*T*winkle, twinkle, little star,
How I wonder what you are!
Up above the world so high,
Like a diamond in the sky.
Twinkle, twinkle, little star,
How I wonder what you are!

Then the traveller in the dark
Thanks you for your tiny spark.
Could he see which way to go,
If you didn't twinkle so?
Twinkle, twinkle, little star,
How I wonder what you are!

Stars shining, number-number one, number two, number three
Good Lord, bye-bye, bye-bye, bye-bye
Good Lord, bye-bye, bye-bye.

Stars shining, number-number four, number five, number six
Good Lord, bye-bye, bye-bye, bye-bye
Good Lord, bye-bye, bye-bye.

Stars shining, number-number seven, number eight, number nine
Good Lord, bye-bye, bye-bye, bye-bye
Good Lord, bye-bye, bye-bye.

Wee Willie Winkie runs through the town,
Upstairs and downstairs in his nightgown,
Rapping at the window, crying through the lock,
Are the children all in bed, for now it's eight o'clock!

*D*iddle, diddle, dumpling, my son John
He went to bed with his trousers on,
One shoe off and the other shoe on,
Diddle, diddle, dumpling, my son John.

Hush, little baby, don't say a word,
Papa's gonna buy you a mocking-bird.

And if that mocking-bird won't sing,
Papa's gonna buy you a diamond ring.

And if that diamond ring is brass,
Papa's gonna buy you a looking-glass.

And if that looking-glass gets broke,
Papa's gonna buy you a billy-goat.

And if that billy-goat don't pull,
Papa's gonna buy you a cart'n'bull.

And if that cart'n'bull turn over,
Papa's gonna buy you a dog named Rover.

And if that dog named Rover don't bark,
Papa's gonna buy you a horse and cart.

And if that horse and cart falls down,
You'll still be the sweetest little baby in town.

"No, no, my Melodies will never die,
While nurses sing, or babies cry."
(From the introduction to an American collection
of nursery rhymes [1833])

The songs and rhymes you will find in this book are often hundreds of years old. These very special relics of earlier times have been passed on from generation to generation and, preserved within them, are many figures, customs and events from history. Although these rhymes were sung by young children at play, with their friends, their nurses or their parents, at home, in the market-place and even in the nurseries of palaces, most of them were not originally written for children. They often originated in malice and irony and spoke about a less than beloved figure from history or life.

This is not, after all, so surprising if we consider that, up to the beginning of this century, children were considered as miniature adults, with the same daily routine as their parents, wearing smaller versions of the same clothes and even going to bed at the same late hour. (Think of the song "Boys and girls, come out to play", which calls the children out to play late at night.) They saw all the cruelty that was part of everyday life in the past. The narrow streets and tiny squares and huddled houses of medieval England left no space for hiding anything from their eyes or ears.

Although there are a number of rhymes whose authors we do know (such as "Mary had a little lamb" which was written by Sarah Josepha Hale of Boston in 1830), the origins of most of them are veiled in mystery.

There are also many different types of rhymes: counting-out rhymes ("Eeny, meeny, miny, mo"); lullabies ("Hush, little baby"); teaching rhymes and memory aids ("Thirty days hath September"); charms ("Rain, rain, go away"); riddles ("Humpty Dumpty") and proverbs ("Go to bed late"); and street-cries ("Hot cross buns"). Others were dancing songs ("Hey diddle, diddle") or made malicious fun of some well-known character ("I do not like thee, Doctor Fell").

p. 4 I won't be my father's Jack. The first names 'Jack' and 'Jill' were commonly used in rhymes and stories to mean man and woman.

p. 6 Eeny, meeny, miny, mo. There are many variants of this rhyme, all related to ancient shepherds' and fishermen's enumeration.

p. 6 Up and down the City Road. This song refers to an old custom. The hatmakers of the town would sell or pledge their tools in pubs over the weekend to get food and drink.

　The Eagle: a pub
　pop: pawn
　weasel: hatmakers' tool
　tuppenny: twopenny
　monkey: a sum of money

p. 7 Hot cross buns was the chant of the pedlars on Good Friday when these hot, fragrant buns were eaten.

p. 7 Rub-a-dub-dub. In the earlier version of the rhyme three ladies were having a bath when these 'respectable' tradesmen peeped in on them. It is their punishment that the rhyme describes.

　rub-a-dub: rubbing the clothes
　turn'em out: turn them out

p. 7 Do you know the muffin man refers to a man selling hot cakes on the street. It is a children's game where one player is blindfolded and then has to catch one of his friends. The child who is caught has then to sing the second verse and the one with the blindfold has to work out who he has caught.

p. 8 Lavender's blue is one of the most ancient love songs and was a dance tune as well.

　'twas: it was
　mine: (here) my

p. 9 See-saw, sacradown, first written down in 1725, is usually sung by children playing on a see-saw, although it probably originated as a song sung by woodcutters as they sawed treetrunks. (The Hungarian equivalent would be *"Hinta-palinta, régi Duna, kiskatona"*.)

p. 9 To market, to market was sung by nurses as they bounced babies on their knees (as with the Hungarian *"Hóc, hóc, katona"*).

p. 9 Ride a cock-horse to Banbury cross refers to Celia Fiennes who often rode to London on horseback, passing through Banbury. Not only was she an excellent rider, but she also dressed very fashionably, wearing little bells on her shoes. The market-place in Banbury had a cross until the Puritans destroyed it in 1601.

p. 11 Rain, rain, go away is an old charm with equivalents in almost every European language (*cf.* Hungarian: *"Süss fel, nap"*).

p. 12 London Bridge is falling down. The game and the song come from the 14th century, but the events they refer to took place in the 11th century. In 1014 the Norwegian Vikings joined forces with the Anglo-Saxons to defeat the Danish Vikings who were occupying London. The Danish warriors stood on the bridge, throwing spears at the Norwegians who pulled down the roofs of nearby houses and cottages to protect their boats and then pulled the bridge down with ropes attached to its underside. There are many sayings, myths and legends connected with bridges, principally because medieval men were afraid of the spirit of the water and believed that bridges, which blocked the spirit's path, made it angry with men.

p. 14 Polly, put the kettle on is a Scottish tune dating back to the end of the 18th century. Polly was a common nickname for girls christened Mary, and Sukey for those christened Susan, among middle-class families.

p. 14 Ring-a-ring o'roses probably refers to the Great Plague of 1630, describing the different stages of this terrible illness. Children dance in a circle, sneezing and tumbling to the ground at the end.

　roses (rosy rash): symptom of the illness

posies: people carried these to ward off the illness
a-tishoo: sneezes, the final symptom
fall down: the infected person, being weak, falls down and dies.

p. 15 *Dance to your daddy* is an old Scottish song.
  lad, laddie: boy
  lass, lassie: girl

p. 15 *Handy Spandy, Jack-a-dandy* was written by Alexander Pope and Philip Carey, ridiculing their fellow poets for the sugary style popular in the 1700s.

p. 16 *This little pig went to market* is probably the most popular toe game and was first written down in 1728 (*cf.* Hungarian "*Ez elment vadászni*").

p. 17 *Jack and Jill went up the hill.*
  water: very precious dew if they climbed the hill for it
  crown: head
  caper: run and jump

p. 18 *Curly Locks* is a courting song from the 19th century.
  wilt thou: will you
  thou shalt: you will
  nor yet: also not

p. 18 *Little Jack Horner* was the servant of an abbot called Richard Whitting. When the abbot sent a pie to Henry VIII, Jack looked into the pie and found the title deeds of twelve manors. He stole one and made his family rich. It was a custom to hide things in pies in those days (16th century).

p. 20 *Old Mother Hubbard* was a popular character in tales and fairground comedies. This version was written by Sarah Catherine Chartin in 1804 and was such a hit that ten thousand copies of its first edition were sold.

p. 22 *I do not like thee, Doctor Fell.* Doctor Fell was the Dean of Christ Church, Oxford.
  thee: you

p. 22 *Old King Cole* was apparently a king in Britain in the 3rd century. He was said to have been very fond of music and his daughter even played the fiddle.

p. 23 *Oh, the grand old Duke of York*, son of George III, was very popular with his soldiers. No one knows anything about the event portrayed in the rhyme.

p. 24 *Humpty Dumpty sat on a wall.* This is a riddle to which the answer is 'egg'. Lewis Carroll also used it in *Through the Looking Glass.*

p. 25 *Hickory, dickory, dock* is a counting rhyme to decide who shall start a game (*cf.* Hungarian "*Ec, pec, kimehetsz*").
  hickory (hevera): 8
  dickory (devera): 9
  dock (dick): 10 in the dialect of shepherds in Westmorland

p. 26 *Baa, baa, black sheep* refers to the taxation of the wool trade which was introduced as early as 1275.

p. 26 *Ladybird, ladybird, fly away home* is a well-known motif in almost every European language. The little insect was believed to be protected by 'Our Lady' (*cf.* Hungarian "*Katalinka, szállj el!*").

p. 27 *Solomon Grundy* dates from 1842 and was used to help children remember the days of the week.

p. 28 *Sing a song of sixpence* dates from the 16th century. Cookbooks of that period mention baked pies containing blackbirds that were supposed to fly away when the pie was cut.

p. 30 *Thirty days hath September* is another teaching rhyme, this time from the 17th century.

p. 30 *A dillar, a dollar* is a mocking rhyme from Yorkshire where a dillar was the name given to dull, stupid boys.

p. 30 *If all the world were paper* probably comes from religious liturgy, as parallels can be found in various religions as well as in the folklore of several countries.

p. 31 *Monday's child is fair of face* shows the belief that there must be some connection between the day on which a child is born and his or her character.
  Sabbath: Sunday
  bonny: pretty
  blithe: merry

p. 32 *A was an apple pie* is an alphabet-teaching rhyme dating from 1641.

p. 33 *Little Miss* (Patience) *Muffet* lived in the 16th century.
  tuffet: a tussock of grass or a small stool
  curds and whey: dessert

p. 34 *There was a crooked man* probably refers to Sir Alexander Leslie of Scotland who made peace with Charles I in 1640, establishing political and religious freedom for Scotland.
  sixpence: probably refers to Charles I
  stile: here, the English-Scottish border

p. 34 *The man in the moon* reflects the belief that an old man lives on the moon, exiled there to carry sticks all his life as a punishment for collecting wood in the forest on Sunday. The rhyme comes from the 18th century.

p. 35 *Hey diddle, diddle* was already a popular dance in 1569.

p. 38 *On the first day of Christmas* comes from 1780 and has a French version as well.

p. 42 *Twinkle, twinkle, little star* was written by Jane Taylor in 1806.

p. 43 *Wee Willie Winkie* was written in 1841 by William Miller.

p. 44 *Diddle, diddle, dumpling.* The first line of this rhyme was the chant of women selling hot dumplings, and nurses or mothers hummed the tune while dressing and undressing their babies.

p. 45 *Hush, little baby* is a lullaby of British origin but has become very popular in the United States.
  mocking-bird: a bird that can imitate the calls of other birds
  looking-glass: mirror
  billy-goat: a male goat

INDEX OF FIRST LINES